The Mirror

Story by June Melser
Illustrations by Bryan Pollard

An old man
found a mirror.
“Oh!” he said.
“It’s a picture
of an old man.”

An old woman
took the mirror.
“No,” she said.
“It’s a picture
of an old woman.”

A young man
took the mirror.
"No," he said.
"It's a picture
of a young man."

A young woman
took the mirror.
“No,” she said.
“It’s a picture
of a young woman.”

“It’s an old man!”
shouted the old man.

“It’s an old woman!”
shouted the old woman.

“It’s a young man!”
shouted the young man.

“It’s a young woman!”
shouted the young woman.

The little girl took the mirror.
She laughed and laughed.

“It’s a happy girl!”
she said.